数学帮帮忙 互动版

上 车 喽！

【美】达芙妮·斯金纳◎著

【美】杰瑞·史麦斯◎绘

袁　颖◎译

我们的旅途 "走走停停"火车时刻表

23次列车：　大湖至科恩德尔

星期四	大湖，缅因州	发车	下午5：30
	雪岸，新罕布什尔州	到站	晚上7：30
		发车	晚上8：00
	米德尔顿，马萨诸塞州	到站	晚上10：00
		发车	晚上10：15
星期五	荷德维尔，弗吉尼亚州	到站	上午11：45
		发车	中午12：30
	坦珀斯，北卡罗来纳州	到站	下午3：30
		发车	下午5：30
	福吉特，南卡罗来纳州	到站	晚上8：00
		发车	晚上9：00
星期六	科恩德尔，佛罗里达州	到站	上午10：30

转乘至太阳城！

24次列车：　科恩德尔至蓝水

星期六	科恩德尔，佛罗里达州	发车	下午3：30
	太阳城，佛罗里达州	到站	下午4：45
		发车	下午5：00
	蓝水，佛罗里达州	到站	下午6：00

天津出版传媒集团

新蕾出版社

献给吉尔·罗森伯格·史麦斯。

——杰瑞·史麦斯

图书在版编目 (CIP) 数据

上车喽！/(美)斯金纳(Skinner,D.)著;(美)
史麦斯(Smath,J.)绘;袁颖译.--天津:新蕾出版
社,2015.12(2024.12 重印)
(数学帮帮忙·互动版)
书名原文:All Aboard!
ISBN 978-7-5307-6314-8

Ⅰ.①上… Ⅱ.①斯…②史…③袁… Ⅲ.①数学-
儿童读物 Ⅳ.①O1-49

中国版本图书馆 CIP 数据核字(2015)第 253572 号

All Aboard! by Daphne Skinner;
Illustrated by Jerry Smath.
Text copyright © 2007 by Kane Press, Inc.
Illustrations copyright © 2007 by Jerry Smath.
All rights reserved, including the right of reproduction in whole or in part in any
form. This edition published by arrangement with Kane Press, Inc. New York, NY,
represented by Lerner Publishing Group through The ChoiceMaker Korea Co.
agency.
Simplified Chinese translation copyright © 2015 by New Buds Publishing House
(Tianjin) Limited Company
ALL RIGHTS RESERVED
本书中文简体版专有出版权经由中华版权代理中心授予新蕾出版社(天津)有
限公司。未经许可,不得以任何方式复制或抄袭本书的任何部分。
津图登字:02-2012-216

出版发行 天津出版传媒集团
新蕾出版社
http://www.newbuds.com.cn
地　　址:天津市和平区西康路 35 号(300051)
出 版 人:马玉秀
电　　话:总编办(022)23332422
　　　　　发行部(022)23332679　23332351
传　　真:(022)23332422
经　　销:全国新华书店
印　　刷:天津新华印务有限公司
开　　本:787mm×1092mm　1/16
印　　张:3
版　　次:2015 年 12 月第 1 版　2024 年 12 月第 22 次印刷
定　　价:12.00 元

无处不在的数学

资深编辑　卢　江

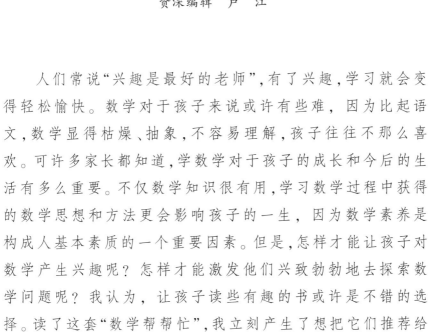

人们常说"兴趣是最好的老师",有了兴趣,学习就会变得轻松愉快。数学对于孩子来说或许有些难,因为比起语文,数学显得枯燥、抽象,不容易理解,孩子往往不那么喜欢。可许多家长都知道,学数学对于孩子的成长和今后的生活有多么重要。不仅数学知识很有用,学习数学过程中获得的数学思想和方法更会影响孩子的一生,因为数学素养是构成人基本素质的一个重要因素。但是,怎样才能让孩子对数学产生兴趣呢?怎样才能激发他们兴致勃勃地去探索数学问题呢?我认为,让孩子读些有趣的书或许是不错的选择。读了这套"数学帮帮忙",我立刻产生了想把它们推荐给教师和家长朋友们的愿望,因为这真是一套会让孩子爱上数学的好书!

这套有趣的图书从美国引进,原出版者是美国资深教育专家。每本书讲述一个孩子们生活中的故事,由故事中出现的问题自然地引入一个数学知识,然后通过运用数学知识解决问题。比如,从帮助外婆整理散落的纽扣引出分类,从为小狗记录藏骨头的地点引出空间方位等等。故事素材全部来源于孩子们的真实生活，不是童话，不是幻想，而是鲜活的生活实例。正是这些发生在孩子身边的故事，让孩子们懂得，数学无处不在并且非常有用；这些鲜活的实例也使得抽象的概念更易于理解，更容易激发孩子学习数学的兴趣，让他们逐渐爱上数学。这样的教育思想和方法与我国近年来提倡的数学教育理念是十分吻合的！

这是一套适合5~8岁孩子阅读的书，书中的有趣情节和生动的插画可以将抽象的数学问题直观化、形象化，为孩子的思维活动提供具体形象的支持。如果亲子共读的话，家长可以带领孩子推测情节的发展，探讨解决难题的办法，让孩子在愉悦的氛围中学到知识和方法。

值得教师和家长朋友们注意的是，在每本书的后面，出版者还加入了"互动课堂"及"互动练习"，一方面通过一些精心设计的活动让孩子巩固新学到的数学知识，进一步体会知识的含义和实际应用；另一方面帮助家长指导孩子阅读，体会故事中数学之外的道理，逐步提升孩子的阅读理解能力。

我相信孩子读过这套书后一定会明白，原来，数学不是烦恼，不是包袱，数学真能帮大忙！

"赶紧上车喽！"列车员大喊。

杰伊和基特在站台上狂奔，他们刚一跳上列车，列车便缓缓开动了。

"多悬啊！"奶奶说，"我还以为自己要一个人去佛罗里达了呢！"

杰伊看看基特说："你就不能准时点吗？"

基特笑了："时间不等人哪！"

爸爸妈妈，再见！

时刻表

3

奶奶很爱坐火车。于是，他们都选择了"走走停停"列车去参加表兄乔的婚礼。

杰伊第一个进了卧铺包厢。"太棒了！"他说。

"看看床铺能从墙壁上折叠下来。"基特说，"太神奇了！"

杰伊看了看他那崭新的带日历的防水手表。"我们很准时，"他说，"16 个小时后将抵达'欢乐奶牛'。"

本次旅程,奶奶、基特和杰伊每人都选了一处要观光的地方。"欢乐奶牛"是杰伊要去的地方。"火车在那里只停靠45分钟。"他说,"所以,我们必须安排好时间,基特。"

基特根本没在听。杰伊叹了口气,拿起菜单:"嗨,餐车营业了!"

"你们俩先去吧。"基特说,"我这就来。"

"好吧。"杰伊知道她一准又会迟到。

"走走停停"火车时刻表

23次列车:　大湖至科恩德尔

星期四	大湖,缅因州	发　车	下午5:30
	雪岸,新罕布什尔州	到　站	晚上7:30
		发　车	晚上8:00
	米德尔顿,马萨诸塞州	到　站	晚上10:00
		发　车	晚上10:15
星期五	荷德维尔,弗吉尼亚州	到　站	上午11:45
		发　车	中午12:30
	坦珀斯,北卡罗来纳州	到　站	下午3:30
		发　车	下午5:30
	福吉特,南卡罗来纳州	到　站	晚上8:00
		发　车	晚上9:00
星期六	科恩德尔,佛罗里达州	到　站	上午10:30

转乘至太阳城!

24次列车:　科恩德尔至蓝水

星期六	科恩德尔,佛罗里达州	发　车	下午3:30
	太阳城,佛罗里达州	到　站	下午4:45
		发　车	下午5:00
	蓝水,佛罗里达州	到　站	下午6:00

基特总是迟到。足球赛迟到，万圣节活动迟到，有一次，甚至连她自己的生日派对也迟到了！

果然，她吃晚饭迟到了。等她慢悠悠地走进餐车时，杰伊已经在吃甜点了。

奶奶把菜单递给基特。"记住，孩子们，"她说，"明天，火车可不会在荷德维尔站停得太久。我们要是磨磨蹭蹭的，就别想去'欢乐奶牛'了。"

"没问题！"杰伊说。

"我无所谓。"基特说。

星期五	荷德维尔，弗吉尼亚州	到 站	上午11:45
		发 车	中午12:30
	坦珀斯，北卡罗来纳州	到 站	下午3:30
		发 车	下午5:30
	福吉特，南卡罗来纳州	到 站	晚上8:00
		发 车	晚上9:00

第二天早上，杰伊早早就把基特叫醒了。他知道基特不会注意到自己起得早，她从来就不看表。

列车刚在荷德维尔站停下来，杰伊就催着奶奶和基特赶紧奔向汽车站。

汽车在 11:50 到站，他们在 12:00 到达"欢乐奶牛"。时间刚刚好！

杰伊的"欢乐奶牛"
时刻表

火车抵达荷德维尔站 11:45
火车从火车站发车   11:50
汽车从火车站发车   12:00
汽车抵达"欢乐奶牛"发车 12:15
汽车从"欢乐奶牛"发车 12:25
汽车抵达火车站   12:30
火车从荷德维尔站发车 12:30

　　杰伊在 12:05 点了一杯软糖奶昔, 奶奶在 12:07
点了一杯蓝莓白果摇摇乐。

　　可基特一直犹豫不决。"猕猴桃葡萄味的?"她
大声念叨着,"香蕉芒果味的?还是香梨薄荷味的?"

基特耽搁得太久，他们差一点儿就错过了返回火车站的汽车。

　　紧接着，汽车被堵在半路上，他们只好一路小跑去赶火车。

　　"太悬了！"杰伊气喘吁吁地说。

　　"难得有机会品尝下'欢乐奶牛'的饮品，"基特说，"我必须选对口味才行。"说着，她吸了一大口，"双倍浆果冰凝乐，真好喝啊！"

当天下午该轮到基特去她想去的地方了。

她最喜欢的魔术师赫科特和鲍勃在北卡罗来纳州的坦珀斯演出。列车在那一站要接上新的客人，所以奶奶、基特和杰伊有足够的时间去观看下午 4:00 的魔术表演。

星期五	荷德维尔，弗吉尼亚州	到站	上午11:45
		发车	中午12:30
	坦珀斯，北卡罗来纳州	到站	下午3:30
		发车	下午5:30
	福吉特，南卡罗来纳州	到站	晚上8:00
		发车	晚上9:00

他们下了火车，奶奶在街上来回看了看。"出租车应该 3:30 就到了。"

"可是，车在哪儿？"基特紧张地问。

"车迟到了。"杰伊说。

"我们要是错过表演可怎么办啊？"基特喊道。

坦珀斯剧场隆重推出

赫科特和鲍勃的
非凡魔术表演！

仅此两天：
3月6日星期四
中午12:00，下午2:00，下午4:00
3月7日星期五
中午12:00，下午2:00，下午4:00，
下午6:00

出租车

　　出租车终于出现了。"对不起，我迟到了。"司机
很抱歉，"今天我晚点了。"

　　基特一头钻进了车里。杰伊还从没见她这么利
索过呢。

　　每当他们在路口等红绿灯的时候，基特都上蹿
下跳地嘟囔着："快呀！快呀！"

赫科特和鲍勃的第一个节目开演的时候，他们刚好落座。

赫科特把鲍勃锯成了两半。

鲍勃从赫科特的鼻子里抽出了一条彩纸。

赫科特把鲍勃变成了一只大猩猩。

鲍勃把赫科特变成了一朵旋风云团，闻起来还带有葡萄汁的味道。

之后，赫科特挑选现场观众上场助演。基特把手臂举得高高的——居然就被选中了！

舞台上，基特手托一顶高帽，赫科特从里面拽出来一只兔子、一个闹钟，还有一条粉色的羽毛长围巾，一切仿佛梦境般美妙。

赫科特和鲍勃把羽毛长围巾和闹钟送给了基特,还有一本他们的新书《赢在计划》。

她幸福得简直要晕过去了。

"演出真是太棒了！"在回去的路上，杰伊说道。

基特仍然沉迷在幸福之中。"说什么我也不会错过这场表演！"她说。这时她想起来了，自己差一点儿就错过了这场演出。

也许计划真的很重要，基特心想。

那天吃晚饭时，基特很准时。

杰伊看了下手表："你准备好了？"

基特只是笑笑。

"明天你们俩也要准时啊。"奶奶说，"别忘了，我们要换乘火车。"

"没错。"杰伊说，"我们会在 10:30 到达科恩德尔，寄存好行李，然后去往您的目的地！"

星期六	科恩德尔，佛罗里达州	到 站	上午10:30

24次列车： 科恩德尔至蓝水

星期	科恩德尔，佛罗里达州	发 车	下午3:30
	太阳城，佛罗里达州	到 站	下午4:45

第二天，基特依然很准时。他们在 10：30 到达科恩德尔站，11：00 正好赶上去往州际博览会的电车。

博览会很是壮观！有骑术表演、游艺项目，还有五个棉花糖摊位，但奶奶的心思全在一件事上。"我们还是直接去参观巨型蔬菜吧。"她说，"听说棒极了！"

州际博览会电车时刻表
星期一至星期五

自火车站发车时间	抵达博览会时间		自博览会发车时间	抵达火车站时间
上午9：00	上午9：30		上午9：30	上午10：00
上午11：00	上午11：30		上午11：30	中午12：00
下午1：00	下午1：30		下午1：30	下午2：00
下午3：00	下午3：30		下午3：30	下午4：00
下午5：00	下午5：30		下午5：30	下午

可展览巨型蔬菜的帐篷还没开始营业。

"我们先去买棉花糖，待会儿再回来。"奶奶说。

"不行。"杰伊对她说，"我们的电车下午 1:30 就要发车了。"

"哦，不！我还想看看巨型墨西哥大辣椒呢！"奶奶看上去失望至极。

自火车站发车时间	抵达博览会时间	自博览会发车时间	抵达火车站时间
上午10:00	上午10:30	上午10:30	上午11:00
上午11:00	上午11:30	上午11:30	中午12:00
中午12:00	中午12:30	中午12:30	下午1:00
下午1:00	下午1:30	下午1:30	下午2:00
下午2:00	下午2:30	下午2:30	下午3:00
下午3:00	下午3:30	下午3:30	下午4:00

"等一下，杰伊！"基特说，她拿出时刻表翻看起来，"你看的是星期一到星期五的时刻表，可今天是星期六。我们可以乘坐下午 2:30 的电车回去，赶上火车应该没有问题。"

杰伊凝视着她，然后自己又查看了一遍时刻表。"我简直不敢相信。"他嘟囔着，"你说得对，基特！"

奶奶激动得大声欢呼："墨西哥大辣椒，我们来啦！"

等待期间，有好多事情可以做呢。

12:00，他们观看了一场驯猪挑战赛。

12:45，奶奶决定参加一场吃馅饼大赛，结果赢得了第二名！

到了下午 1:30,该去参观巨型蔬菜了。那些家伙可真是令人目瞪口呆。一等奖花落一只红萝卜,那萝卜大得像个沙滩皮球。奶奶、基特和杰伊还和大萝卜合影留念呢。

　　下午2:30, 他们乘电车赶回火车站。3:30,他们转乘了新的列车。

火车在下午 4：45 抵达佛罗里达州的太阳城。天空阴云密布。杰伊、基特和爸爸妈妈在阳光酒店会合时，天开始下起雨来。

阳光酒店

24次列车： 科恩德尔至蓝水

星期六	科恩德尔，佛罗里达州	发车	下午3：30
	太阳城，佛罗里达州	到站	下午4：45
		发车	下午5：00
	蓝水，佛罗里达州	到站	下午6：00

　　当晚，在孩子们睡觉前，奶奶问道："婚礼是明天上午 10:00。我们什么时候出发呢，杰伊？"

　　"如果能在9:30准时出门最好。"他瞟了一眼基特。

　　"没问题。"她说。

  第二天一早,杰伊被一阵巨大的声响惊醒。鼓声?不是。动物们惊慌逃跑的声音?不是。他环顾四周。外面的阳光很明亮!现在几点了?

  "杰伊?"基特喊道。她咚咚敲门,"杰伊,快起床啦!"

杰伊从床上一跃而起，"我的闹钟怎么没响啊？"

"别紧张，"基特说，"时间还早。昨晚下雨导致断电，闹钟一个也响不了了。"

杰伊眨眨眼睛："那你是怎么醒的？"

"我有魔法。"她说着，咯咯笑了起来，"赫科特和鲍勃给我的闹钟是用电池的！现在，我们去把大家都叫起来吧。我们可不想在婚礼上迟到，对吧？"

的确应该感谢基特，他们没有迟到。

时 刻 表

你能竖着读吗？你能横着读吗？

太棒了！你能看懂列车时刻表了！

假设你要乘坐海滩特快从贝壳城前往海豚湾，计划星期五出发，星期六到达。

海滩特快时刻表

15次列车： 城堡坡至海豚湾

第一步：竖向找到星期五，横向找到贝壳城。	星期五	🏰	城堡坡	发车	下午5:30
第二步：找到发车栏。然后横向找到发车时间。		🐚	贝壳城	到站 发车	下午6:00 下午6:15
		☀	桑尼维尔	到站 发车	晚上9:00 晚上10:00
第三步：竖向找到星期六，横向找到海豚湾。	星期六	⛵	水手湾	到站 发车	上午6:00 上午6:05
		🗼	灯 塔	到站 发车	上午8:30 上午9:00
第四步：找到到站栏。然后横向找出列车抵达海豚湾的时间。		🐬	海豚湾	到站	上午10:00

就你的旅程回答下列问题：

1. 你哪天出发？

2. 你从哪个城市出发？

3. 列车几点发车？

4. 你的列车哪天到达？

5. 终点站是哪个城市？

6. 你到达终点站的时间？

答案：1. 星期五 2. 贝壳城 3. 下午6:15 4. 星期六
5. 海豚湾 6. 上午10:00

32

亲爱的家长朋友,请您和孩子一起完成下面这些内容,会有更大的收获哟!

提高阅读能力

- 看看封面,读读标题。标题是什么意思？让孩子猜想一下故事会讲些什么呢？
- 一起阅读故事。为什么开始时奶奶担心自己要一个人去佛罗里达了呢？杰伊怎么知道餐车开始营业了？
- 看第 20 页和第 23 页。为什么说会阅读时刻表非常重要？你觉得基特从今以后会认真留意时刻表了吗？为什么呢？

巩固数学概念

- 请看扉页上"走走停停"列车时刻表中 23 次列车的运行情况。它是从星期几开始发车的？从哪个城市首发？列车会在星期五首先到达哪里？23 次列车的终点站是哪里？在星期几、什么时间到站？

- 请看这张时刻表中 24 次列车的运行情况。基特、杰伊和奶奶要在哪个城市换乘？24 次列车要开多久才能到达太阳城？（提示：请留意列车到达太阳城的时间。）

- 附加题：假设婚礼的举办地是蓝水，那么基特、杰伊和奶奶要花多长时间从科恩德尔抵达蓝水？

- 参看第 32 页上的时刻表。假设你要乘下午 5：30 的火车从城堡坡赶往贝壳城。你最好在什么时间抵达车站？（开放性答案，可将交通拥堵、排队购票等因素考虑在内。）

生活中的数学

- 针对不同的时刻表展开讨论，可由书中涉及的不同类型的时刻表展开。帮助孩子针对自己的学习生活制订作息表，内容可包括起床、吃早饭和上学等活动的时间。

- 鼓励孩子制订一周时间表，说不定孩子会愿意将周末的活动安排也一起写进去呢！

小朋友们，书中教给了我们看时刻表的方法，你学会了吗？

车次	始发	经由	经由	终到
G476	荣成 8:40	威海 9:06	济南 13:19	北京南 15:18
G475	北京南 15:36	济南 17:47	威海 21:50	荣成 22:20
G458	荣成 13:20	威海 13:41	济南 17:45	上海虹桥 22:18
G456	上海虹桥 6:20	济南 10:37	威海 14:51	荣成 15:15
D6076	荣成 14:00	威海 14:21	莱阳 15:48	济南 18:34

我在荣成，如果我想去北京，应该乘坐哪趟列车呢？请选择正确答案并涂上红色。

如果是去上海呢？请选择正确答案并涂上绿色。

聪明的小朋友们，快来帮帮忙吧！

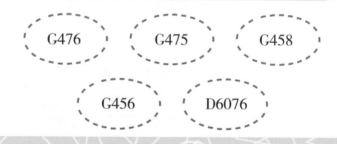

G476　　　　G475　　　　G458

G456　　　　D6076

K8261	济南—文登	发车	00:50
		到站	07:57
	文登—威海	发车	07:59
		到站	08:39

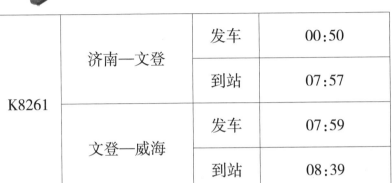

要去看大海了，真让人开心！
我乘坐的这趟火车从济南到威海大约要几小时呢？请选择正确答案并涂上红色。

7个小时　　8个小时　　9个小时

小朋友们,欢迎来到海洋剧场!现在是下午4点,精彩的节目马上开始!

白鲸表演了 15 分钟,太精彩啦!

海豚真是太聪明啦!几只海豚轮番表演了 20 分钟!

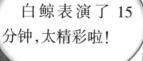

小企鹅实在是太可爱了,它们也进行了 10 分钟的表演!

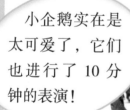

算一算,整场节目一共演了( )分钟。

我们要去赶乘下午 5:40 的火车,来得及吗?

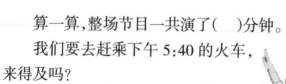

海边的活动太丰富了，不知不觉中，在海边就度过了半天……

沙滩排球 9:30

经过了（ ）分钟

垒城堡 10:00

游泳 11:00

经过了（ ）小时

经过了（ ）小时

吹海风 12:00

从宾馆到火车站需要 40 分钟，咱们要坐今天下午 5:00 的火车继续旅行,应该几点出门呢?

放心吧！我早就计划好了！

他们下午几点出门合适呢?

3:00　　　4:00　　　5:00

我要感谢《赢在计划》这本书，做事情前先做好计划也很重要呀！

是啊，会看时刻表对于旅行真的很重要！

我们的火车之旅真是太愉快啦！

杰伊、基特和奶奶又要开始新的旅行啦！基特从这次的旅行中感到"做好计划真的很重要"！小朋友们，你们是不是也有这样的感觉呢？

那就动动手，为自己也制订一份时间计划表吧！

互动练习1：
（逆时针顺序）

5 时 30 分

10 时 30 分

6 时

5 时 45 分

12 时

互动练习2：

红色：G476

绿色：G458

互动练习3：

8 个小时

互动练习4：

45

赶乘下午 5:40 的火车来得及。

互动练习5：

30

1

1

互动练习6：

可以提前 1 个小时出门,选择下午 4:00。

互动练习7：

略。

（习题设计：孙欣萌）

All Aboard!

"All aboard!" the conductor shouted.

Jay and Kit raced down the platform and climbed on—just before the train chugged off.

"That was close!" said their grandma. "I was afraid I'd have to go to Florida all alone!"

Jay looked at Kit. "Can't you ever be on time?"

Kit laughed. "Time shmime!"

Gram loved trains, so they were all taking the Stop-n-Go Railway to Cousin Jo's wedding.

Jay got to the roomette first. "Cool!" he said.

"Look how the beds fold out of the wall," said Kit. "It's like magic."

Jay checked his new waterproof calendar watch. "We're on schedule," he said. "We'll be at the Happy Cow in about sixteen hours."

Gram, Kit, and Jay had each chosen a place to visit on their trip. The Happy Cow was Jay's. "The train only stops for 45 minutes," he said. "So our timing has to be perfect, Kit."

Kit wasn't listening. Jay sighed and picked up the menu. "Hey, the dining car is open!"

"You two go ahead," said Kit. "I'll catch up."

"Uh huh." Jay knew she'd be late.

Kit was late a lot. She was late for soccer games. She was late for trick or treating. One time, she was even late for her own birthday party!

And she was late getting to dinner.

When she finally strolled in, Jay was already on dessert.

Gram gave Kit a menu. "Remember, kids," she said, "the train won't stop long in Herdville tomorrow. If we dawdle, we'll never get to the Happy Cow."

"No problem!" Jay said.

"Whatever," said Kit.

The next morning, Jay woke Kit up extra early. He knew she wouldn't notice. She never looked at clocks.

When the train stopped in Herdville, he rushed Gram and Kit to the bus stop.

The bus pulled up at 11:50, and they got to the Happy Cow at 12:00. Perfect timing !

Jay ordered a Fast-Track Fudge milkshake at 12:05. Grandma ordered her Blueberry-Gingko Memory Waker at 12:07.

But Kit just couldn't make up her mind. "Kiwi-Grape?" she wondered out loud. "Banana–Mango? Peppermint–Pear?"

Kit took so long that they almost missed the bus back to the station.

Then the bus got caught in traffic, and they had to run for their train.

"That was way too close!" panted Jay.

"It was my one chance to have a Happy Cow shake," Kit said. "I had to pick just the right flavor." She took a big slurp. "Double-Berry Slow-Melt Brain Freezer—yum."

That afternoon was Kit's big stop.

Her favorite magicians, Hector and Bob, were performing in Tempus, North Carolina. The train was stopping there to pick up new passengers. So Gram, Kit, and Jay had just enough time to see the 4:00 magic show.

When they got off the train, Gram looked up and down the street. "The taxi was supposed to be here at 3:30."

"Well , where is it ? " asked Kit nervously.

"It's late," said Jay.

"What if we miss the show? " Kit cried.

The taxi finally showed up. "Sorry I'm late," said the driver. "I'm behind schedule today."

Kit scrambled inside. Jay had never seen her move so fast.

Every time they stopped for a light, Kit bounced up and down and whispered, "Hurry up! Hurry up!"

They got to their seats just as Hector and Bob were doing their first trick.

Hector sawed Bob in half.

Bob pulled a scarf out of Hector's nose.

Hector changed Bob into a gorilla.

Bob changed Hector into a whirling cloud that smelled like grape juice.

Then Hector asked for volunteers. Kit's arm shot up—and he chose her!

Up on the stage, Kit held a top hat as Hector pulled out a rabbit, a clock, and a pink feather boa. It was like a wonderful dream.

Hector and Bob gave Kit the boa, the clock, and their new book, *Timing is Everything.*

She practically fainted.

"That was cool! " Jay said on the way back.

Kit was still in a happy daze. "I wouldn't have missed it for anything," she said. Then she remembered. She almost had missed it.

Maybe timing is everything, Kit thought.

That night, Kit was right on time for dinner.

Jay checked his watch. "You're ready?"

Kit just smiled.

"Better be on time tomorrow, you two," Gram said. "Don't forget—we're switching trains."

"Right , " said Jay . " We get to Corndale at 10:30 and find lockers for our bags. And then we visit your special stop!"

The next day, Kit was right on time again. They pulled into Corndale at exactly 10:30 and caught the State Fair Trolley at 11:00.

The fair was huge! There were rides, and games, and five cotton candy booths—but Gram's mind was on just one thing. "Let's head right over to the Giant Vegetables," she said. "I hear they're amazing!"

But the Giant Vegetable tent was closed.

"We'll just get some cotton candy and come back later," said Gram.

" We can't , " Jay told her. "Our trolley leaves at 1:30."

"Oh, no! I wanted to see the giant jalapeño!"Gram looked very disappointed

"Wait, Jay!" said Kit. She took the schedule and flipped it over. "You're reading the Monday to Friday side. Today's Saturday. We can get a trolley at 2:30 and still be back in time to catch our train."

Jay stared at her. Then he checked the schedule for himself. "I can't believe it," he murmured. "You're right, Kit!"

Gram whooped. "Jalapeño, here we come!"

There was lots to do while they waited.

At 12:00 they watched a champion hog-caller.

At 12:45 Gram decided to enter a pie-eating contest. She came in second!

At 1:30 it was time to see the giant vegetables. They were amazing. First prize went to a radish as big as a beach ball. Gram, Kit, and Jay had their picture taken with it.

At 2:30 they took the trolley back to the station. And at 3:30 they got on their new train.

The train stopped in Sunny City, Florida, at 4:45. It was cloudy. Jay and Kit met their parents at the Sunny Suites Inn—just as it started to rain.

Before the kids went to bed that night, Gram said, "The wedding's at 10:00 tomorrow. When should we be ready to leave, Jay?"

"We'll be fine if we're out the door at 9:30—on the dot." He glanced at Kit.

"Not a problem," she said.

The next morning, Jay woke up to a loud thumping noise. Drum? No. Stampede? No. He looked around. The sun was so bright outside! What time was it?

"Jay?" Kit called. She thumped on his door again. "Jay! Wake up!"

Jay bolted out of bed. "Why didn't my alarm clock go off?"

"Relax," Kit said. "It's still early. The rain last night made the power go out. No alarms rang."

Jay blinked. "So how come you're awake?"

"Magic," she said, grinning. "The clock Hector and Bob gave me works on batteries! Now, let's wake everyone up. We don't want to be late for the wedding, do we?"

And thanks to Kit, they weren't.